D1283757

M 1734 .E45
Eisler, Hanns, 1898-1962.
Songs of Bertolt Brecht and
   Hanns Eisler 46325

SONGS OF BERTOLT BRECHT and HANNS EISLER

Bertolt Brecht

Hanns Eisler

Eric Bentley

Earl Robinson

Songs of BERTOLT BRECHT and HANNS EISLER

Edited by ERIC BENTLEY

Forty-two songs in German and English, edited, with singable English translations and introductory notes by Eric Bentley.
Music edited by Earl Robinson.
With piano arrangements and guitar chords.

OAK PUBLICATIONS   NEW YORK, N.Y.

WITHDRAWN
COLLEGE
BAYTOWN, TEXAS

Production and Design: Jean Hammons and
Irwin Silber

Music Autography: Carl Rosenthal

FIRST PRINTING

Eric Bentley's editorial matter, and his English lyrics, are copyright
© 1967 by Eric Bentley, except where previous protection of individ-
ual items is indicated on the first page of such item.

© 1967 by OAK PUBLICATIONS, INC., 701 Seventh Ave.,
New York, N. Y. 10036. All rights reserved.

Library of Congress Card Catalogue # 66-19062

Printed in the United States of America for the Publisher by Faculty Press, Inc., Brooklyn, N. Y.   OFFSET—PRINTING 159

WITHDRAWN

83.654
E36
461.325

FOR GEORG EISLER and WOLF BIERMANN

7-25-68 Direct 10.00

CONTENTS

From THE MEASURES TAKEN

From THE MOTHER

From THE GOOD WOMAN

From ROUND HEADS

From THE MASTER RACE

From SCHWEYK

FOREWORD

by Eric Bentley

Looking recently through various collections of "songs of labor and freedom" I was amazed how very few new tunes there are are in them -- and by new I only mean as new as the lyrics. A tremendous number -- I hesitate to suggest a percentage -- are set to familiar, or at least old, tunes. So many, indeed, are set to hymn tunes that one realizes that politics, even in the broadest sense of the term, has not yet proved anything like as inspiring, musically, as religion used to be. Nor am I thinking of musical masterpieces. I am thinking of, for example, such a modest affair as "Hold the Fort," which is now the tune of a Union song, but which my grandmother knew from her Sankey and Moody hymn book. Can no trade union discover within itself the musical afflatus of Sankey and Moody?

There is one man, and perhaps only one, who in our time has himself created a large body of admirable political songs: Hanns Eisler. Is the achievement so unusual that we cannot even recognize it when we see it? For certainly this body of work is not widely known.

As far as the United States is concerned, the reason for a certain coolness to Eisler has to do with his politics, and those of his brother Gerhard and his sister Ruth. But even if it were reasonable to punish Hanns Eisler on this account, it seems odd that we should punish ourselves by denying ourselves the pleasure that his music undeniably and irresistibly conveys.

Are the songs in this book Communist propaganda? Had the question been put to Brecht and Eisler they might have answered: Well, we hope so! But will these songs be received as such by most people who will hear them? By Communists, yes: but what use is preaching to the converted? And those who make out of opposition to Communism their whole emotional life will force these songs to help them pursue their life's purpose and will not be interested in finding in them anything but the Enemy.

Everyone else, though, it seems to me, can be far more comfortable and relaxed about this matter. Must propaganda for a cause one has not espoused, and may dissent from, necessarily offend one? By no means. I am not offended by a Salvation Army rally, and it is not because I despise the Salvation Army; I don't. I do despise -- or at any rate loathe -- the sentiments expressed in "The Marseillaise," but I am afraid this does not stop me also finding it a stirring song: I am glad not to be ignorant of it. And couldn't many who find some of Eisler's views contemptible or loathsome be glad, nonetheless, not to be ignorant of his songs? I rather think some of Eisler's songs -- "Comintern*," perhaps, "Song of the United Front," surely -- have the historic glamour and significance of a "Marseillaise" or an "Internationale." Shouldn't we know those, as we know these?

I am defending Eisler on what, to many in the U.S., must seem his more vulnerable side. Only a minority of his songs need that kind of defense. There is nothing specifically "Communist" about the majority of them. They stand or fall by the same criteria we apply to any other composer. Here the only possible complaint is not against Eisler but against ourselves for not giving his songs a chance. Not having been heard, they have been ignored. What I would contend is that, once they are heard, they can never be ignored again. My record album Songs of Hanns Eisler, was a deliberate, if small-scale, attempt to see that Eisler got heard. Possibly some listeners thought that they could have sung the songs better themselves -- if only the words and the music were available. With the publication of the present volume, the words and music *are* available; and all who think they can sing the songs of Hanns Eisler "better themselves" are free to try it.

* Not in this volume because the words are not by Brecht.

ACKNOWLEDGEMENTS

My greatest debt is naturally to Bertolt Brecht and Hanns Eisler, both of whom I first met some time in the winter of 1941-2 in Los Angeles, and whom I continued to see, intermittently, till their respective deaths. Whatever understanding I have gained of their songs I gained, if not from the songs themselves, from their creators.

The present volume grew gradually out of my work as a Brecht translator and then, more specifically, out of my efforts to sing the songs and so, perforce, to make English versions that can be sung. I had many collaborators along the way, for the music had to be copied, transposed, and, sometimes, simplified. Let me here thank Patia Rosenberg and Eric Regener for their share in the work.

Christopher McMillan helped me see the volume through the press. Earl Robinson not only did his own job but helped me solve some of the many problems of properly suiting the word to the note. Irwin Silber of Oak Publications was the man who insisted on the volume being done in the first place and who then saw the job through with much enthusiasm.

Eric Bentley
New York City
Fall, 1966

NOTES ON THE MUSIC

by Earl Robinson

Here is a man operating in our time with a sure knowledge of the classics but having known, loved, and studied with Arnold Schoenberg, the great composer and founder of the twelve-tone method. No stranger to the symphony and the larger choral work, he has also written prolifically for piano and all the usual chamber music combinations (as well as many unusual) ones. His larger works for stage and film include several excellent scores done for Hollywood features in the Forties while he was here in exile from Nazism. Perhaps, however, he spoke most importantly both to individuals and mass audiences all over the world through his songs. These may be complex and dissonant, as with the three entitled "To Those Who Come After." Or they may be so well designed for mass singing that the absence of an accompaniment is not noticed. (As Eisler once said: "Workers don't carry a piano around with them.") To the Brechtian qualities of sardonic humor, didacticism, truth, and humanity, Eisler lends an enormous strength and compassion. In fact, one must say the combination of simplicity and power, so foreign to much of the music of the 20th Century, is the outstanding feature of the songs in this book.

Eisler was steeped in the folk music of Germany, peasant songs of love and struggle which inspired his great predecessors including Bach, Brahms and Beethoven.

I shall direct my notes to people who would not ordinarily come in contact with music like Hanns Eisler's - or words like Brecht's, for that matter. I start out by assuming that they know the basic chords, major and minor, in the keys of A,B,C,D,E,F & G, and that they can use a capo*. Also that they can read and figure out a chord diagram. But I am allowing for those who do not read music. Eisler is a sophisticated composer and did not conceive most of his songs for guitar accompaniment; nevertheless, all but three of the songs in this book can be done with guitar, and if you are willing to work and puzzle your way through, you are in for a wonderful musical experience, besides increasing your skill and knowledge considerably.

There are more than a hundred and twenty-five diagrams of chords not commonly confronted in standard chord charts. The diagrams indicate the number of strings to pluck and usually the simplest way of playing the chord. Here are some helps to understanding and using them Pluck only strings 1, 3 & 4 here, holding index finger on 1st fret of 1st string and middle or ring finger on 3rd fret of 4th string. Skip the strings with an X above.

Generally a chord listed simply as E⁷ will be the E seventh chord in the basic

10

root position, that is, E is the lowest sound in the chord. But inversions of chords are often very important to the proper sound and voice leading of the bass line. So, whenever useful I have indicated the inversions of the chord (plus a diagram) as follows:

1st Inversion (3rd of chord in bass) = E   (or any Em
                                                III   chord) iii

2nd Inversion (5th of chord in bass) = E   Em
                                                V   v

3rd Inversion (7th in bass)   =   E   Em
                                            VII   vii

4th Inversion (9th in bass)   =   E9   Em
                                            IX   ix

⌒ = Barre. First finger holds down 4, 5 or 6 strings (acting like a capo) leaving the other fingers free to fret where needed. There are few barred chords used however because the aim has been simplicity. Augmented chords use + i.e. A flat augmented is A$^\flat$+, A augmented seventh is A+^{7}, etc. Diminished chords use °, i.e. F° is F diminished, etc.

Many Eisler chords omit the third, This is indicated by F(no3). Other chords omit the third and put in the 4th or 2nd. This is indicated by F(+4) or F(+2). Don't confuse these with the Augmented+. These are always in parentheses () Sometimes the 5th (or 9th) is flatted. This is indicated as follows B$^\flat$7 ($^{\flat 5}$)or Am$^{\flat 9}$. Some chords are written simply as single notes an octave apart (no 3rd no 5th). They should be played then generally without 3 or 5 and are indicated A(open)

If it is not clear whether a chord is major or minor, with Eisler it is usually minor. Pay special attention to the note at bottom of page 144. It applies not only to the song "In Praise Of Study" but to a large number of songs in the book. Many of Eisler's accompaniments consists of a simple marching beat and economy is most important. Use 2, 3 & 4 string chords rather than trying to cover all six strings.

Finally, single and double string trills, and counter-melodies may be worked out effectively in many places. As a contrast to the rhythmic plucking of chords a single melody, perhaps following the bass line, will often be effective, and I am sure Eisler would have approved, if you do it with taste and respect.

* movable bridge to clamp across your strings at any fret, allowing the performer to transpose difficult keys into easier playing and singing ones. (Cost about $1.50)

Coal for Mike

Kohlen für Mike

Words by Bertolt Brecht; Music by Hanns Eisler;
English lyrics by Eric Bentley; © 1967 by Eric Bentley.

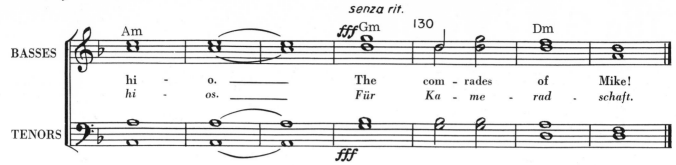

The Gray Goose

Die haltbare Graugans

Words by Bertolt Brecht; Music by Hanns Eisler;
English lyrics by Eric Bentley; ©1967 by Eric Bentley.

If it is desired to imitate the piano part on guitar, note the diagrams which may be noodled (trilled with thumb and index finger)
on the first and second string - back and forth as fast as you can.
Where the accompaniment gets more complicated, use the chords
indicated, arpeggio style.

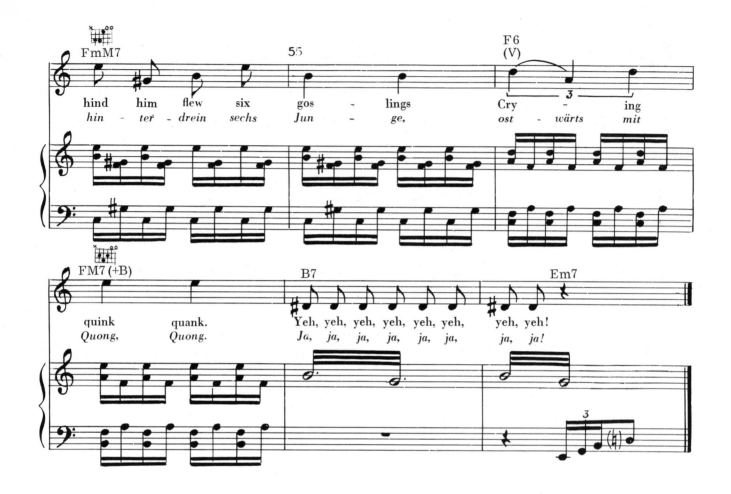

hind him flew six gos - lings Cry - ing
hin - ter - drein sechs Jun - ge, ost - wärts mit

quink quank. Yeh, yeh, yeh, yeh, yeh, yeh, yeh, yeh!
Quong, Quong. Ja, ja, ja, ja, ja, ja, ja, ja!

Solidarity Song

Solidaritätslied

Words by Bertolt Brecht; Music by Hanns Eisler;
English lyrics by Eric Bentley; ©1967 by Eric Bentley.

worth In fam - ine and in plen - ty:
stellt beim Hun - gern und beim Es - sen,

Whose to - mor - row is to - mor - row And whose earth is the earth?
wes - sen Mor - gen ist der Mor - gen wes - sen Welt ist die Welt?

And our various lords and masters
Welcome our disunity
For so long as they divide us
Lords and masters they shall be.

Black and white and brown and yellow,
End the rule of sword and gun!
For when once you raise your voices
All the peoples shall be one.

Unsere Herrn, wer sie such seien,
Sehen unsere Zwietracht gern
Denn solang sie uns entzweien
Bleiben sie doch unsere Herrn.

Schwarzer, Weisser, Brauner, Gelber!
Endel ihre Schlächterein!
Reden erst die Völker selber,
Werden sie schnell einig sein.

Song of the United Front

Das Einheitsfrontlied

Words by Bertolt Brecht; Music by Hanns Eisler;
English lyrics by Eric Bentley; © 1967 by Eric Bentley.

not a wor-ker too? Join up in the wor-kers' u-
Platz, Ge - nos - se ist! Reih dich ein in die Ar - bei - ter -

nit - ed front! Com-rade, here's the place for you! And you.
ein - heits - front, weil du auch ein Ar - bei - ter bist! Und bist!

A man's a man and therefore
He'd rather not be trampled underfoot.
He wants no master over him,
And no slave under his boot.

A wage slave is a wage slave,
And no one else will end his slavery.
And therefore only the working class
Can set the worker free.

Und weil der Mensch ein Mensch ist,
drum hat er Stiefel im Gesicht nicht gern,
er will unter sich keine Sklaven sehn
und uber sich keinen Herrn.

Und weil der Prolet ein Prolet ist,
drum wird ihn kein anderer befrein,
es kann die Befreiung der Arbeiter nur
das Werk der Arbeiter sein.

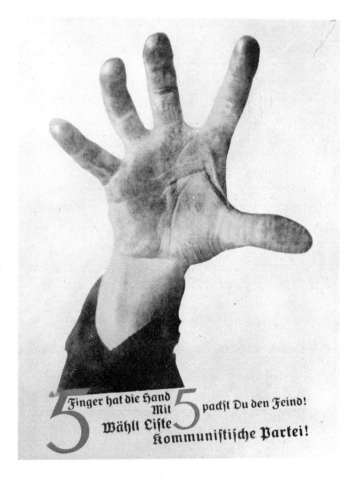

All or Nothing

Sklave, wer wird dich befreien?

Words by Bertolt Brecht; Music by Hanns Eisler; English lyrics by Eric Bentley; ©1965 by Folkways Records.

Who'll avenge your scars and bruises?
You on whom the blows descended
Are by all the weak befriended.
We'll decide who wins, who loses:
We'll avenge your scars and bruises.
    So it's all or nothing.   None or everyone.
    One man cannot rescue any.
    But many can rescue many.
    For it's all or nothing.   None or everyone.

Who will dare? you ask in sorrow.
He whose misery's past bearing,
Finding finally the daring,
Joins with those who are declaring:
We won't wait until tomorrow.
    So it's all or nothing.   None or everyone.
    One man cannot rescue any.
    But many can rescue many.
    For it's all or nothing.   None or everyone.

Wer, Geschlagner, wird dich rächen?
Du, dem sie den Schlag versetzten,
Reih dich ein mit den Verletzten
Wir, in allen unsern Schwächen
Werden, Kamerad, dich rächen.
    Keiner oder Alle! Alles oder Nichts!
    Einer kann sich da nicht retten.
    Gewehre oder Ketten!
    Keiner oder Alle! Alles oder Nichts!

Wer, Verlorner, wird es wagen?
Wer sein Elend nicht mehr tragen kann
Muss sich zu jenen schlagen
Die aus Not schon dafür sorgen
Dass es heut heisst und nicht morgen.
    Keiner oder Alle! Alles oder Nichts!
    Einer kann sich da nicht retten.
    Gewehre oder Ketten!
    Keiner oder Alle! Alles oder Nichts!

Peace Song

Friedenslied

Words by Bertolt Brecht; Music by Hanns Eisler;
English lyrics by Eric Bentley; © 1964 by Eric Bentley.

Ballad of the Soldier

Ballade vom Soldaten

Words by Bertolt Brecht; Music by Hanns Eisler;
English lyrics by Eric Bentley; © 1955, 1959, 1961, 1962,
1963 by Eric Bentley.

Guitar may play chords in parentheses and capo up one fret if
desired.

want my ad - vice said the wise wom-an to the sol - dier.
weg 's ist nicht weis'! sag - te das Weib zum Sol - da - ten.

Più mosso

But that young sol - dier he load - ed his gun And he
Doch der Sol - dat mit der Ku - gel im Lauf, And der

reached for his knife and he start - ed to run: For
hör - te die Trom - mel und lach - te dar - auf, mar -

march - ing For march - ing ne - ver could hurt
schie - ren, mar - schie - ren kann nim - mer mehr scha -

Woe to him who defies the advice of the
  wise!
If you wade in the water 'twill drown you.
Don't ignore what I say or you'll rue it
  one day,
Said the wise woman to the soldier.

But the young soldier, his knife at his
  side,
And his gun in his hand, he steps into
  the tide
For water never could hurt him.
When the new moon is shining on shingle
  roofs white
We are all coming back, go and pray for
  that night
That's what the soldiers told the woman.

Then the wise woman spoke: You will
  vanish like smoke
And your glorious deeds will not warm
  me
And just watch the smoke fly! O God
  don't let him die!
Said the wise woman to the soldier.

But the young soldier his knife at his side
And his gun in his hand is swept out by the
  tide
He waded in the water and it drowned him.
And the lad who defied the wise woman's
  advice
When the new moon shone floated down
  with the ice.
So what could the soldiers tell the woman?

The wise woman spoke: he has vanished
  like smoke
And his glorious deeds did not warm you!
You ignored what I say and you rue it
  today!
Said the wise woman to all the soldiers.

Ach, bitter bereut, wer des Weisen Rat
  scheut
Und vom Alter sich nicht lässt beraten!
Ach, zu hoch nicht hinaus, es geht übel
  aus!
Sagte das Weib zum Soldaten.

Doch der Soldat mit dem Messer im Gurt
Lacht ihr kalt ins Gesicht und ging über
  die Furt
Was konnte das Wasser ihm schaden?
Wenn weiss der Mond überm Mongefluss
  steht
Kommen wir wieder; nimm's auf ins
  Gebet!
Sagten zum Weib die Soldaten.

Ihr vergeht wie der Rauch, und die
  Wärme geht auch
Und uns wärmen nicht eure Taten!
Ach, wie schnell geht der Rauch! Gott,
  behüte ihn auch!
Sagte das Weib vom Soldaten.

Und der Soldat mit dem Messer am Gurt
Sank hin mit dem Speer, und mit riss ihn
  die Furt
Und das Wasser frass auf, die drin waten.
Kuhl stand der Mond überm Mongefluss
  weiss
Doch der Soldat trieb hinab mit dem Eis
Und was sagten dem die Soldaten?

Er verging wie der Rauch, und die Wärme
  ging auch
Und es wärmten sie nicht seine Taten.
Ach bitter bereut, wer des Weibes Rat
  scheut!
Sagte das Weib zum Soldaten.

To the Little Radio

An den kleinen Radioapparat

Words by Bertolt Brecht; Music by Hanns Eisler;
English lyrics by Eric Bentley; ©1963 by Eric Bentley.

It is possible for a resourceful guitarist to approach the exact sound of the accompaniment in this lovely little song, particularly by playing the bass notes (on the bottom bass staff) down an octave and using only strings 1 and 2 above. Because of the constantly changing pattern, the chords indicated can only give an approximation.

O lit - tle box I car - ried in my flight so as not to
Du klei - ner Ka - sten, den ich flüch - tend trug, dass mei - ne

break the rad- io tubes in - side me from house to boat, from boat to train held
Lam - pen mir auch nicht zer - brä - chen, be - sorgt vom Haus zum Schiff, vom Schiff zum

tight, so that my en - e -mies could still ad - dress me,
Zug, dass mei - ne Fein - de wei - ter zu mir sprä - chen,

And the Times are Dark and Fearful

Und es sind die finstern Zeiten

Words by Bertolt Brecht; Music by Hanns Eisler:
English lyrics by Eric Bentley; ©1967 by Eric Bentley.

Cm7   15

Yet their hearts are   deft - ly man – aged   and their smiles are   soft. __
Doch das Herz bleibt schnell ge - re – gelt   und das Lä - cheln weich. __

The Homecoming

Die Heimkehr

Words by Bertolt Brecht; Music by Hanns Eisler;
English lyrics by Eric Bentley; © 1963 by Eric Bentley.

Guitar plays chords in parentheses and capos up three frets.

Easter Sunday, 1935

Ostersonntag

Words by Bertolt Brecht; Music by Hanns Eisler;
English lyrics by Eric Bentley; ©1963 by Eric Bentley.

A Hollywood Elegy

Words by Bertolt Brecht; Music by Hanns Eisler;
© 1967 by Oak Publications.

To Those Who Come After:
Three Elegies

Words by Bertolt Brecht; Music by Hanns Eisler;
English lyrics by Eric Bentley; ©1963 by Eric Bentley.

I

46,325

LEE COLLEGE LIBRARY
BAYTOWN, TEXAS

-51-

man who laughs ___ has ___ mere-ly not ___ re - ceived the fright-ful
La - chen-de ___ hat die furcht-ba - re Nach-richt nur noch nicht emp -

news ___ What a time this is when if we talk of ___
fan - gen. ___ Was sind das für Zei - ten, wo ein Ge - spräch ü - ber

trees that's all but a crime be-cause we are si - lent a-bout ___ at-roc -
Bäu - me fast ein Ver - bre - chen ist, weil es Schwei - gen ü - ber so viel Un-tat

it - ies. That man calm-ly ___ walk - ing a -
ein-schliesst. Der dort ru-hig ___ ü - ber die

time ___ of dark ___ ness!
fin - ste - ren Zei - ten.

II

Moderately

time that was giv - en me on earth. ____
Zeit, *die auf* *Er - den* *mir* *ge - ge - ben war.* ____

III

Do not drag - Andante

You who'll be borne up out ____ of the
Ihr, *die ihr* *auf - tau - chen wer - det aus der*

flood in which we have gone ___ down, ___ re - call when you speak of our
Flut, in der wir un - ter - ge - gan - gen sind, *be - denkt, wenn ihr von un - ser'n*

weak - ness - es the ___ dark time, the dark ___ time ___ you es - caped.
Schwä - chen sprecht, auch der *fin - ste - ren Zeit, der ihr ent - ron - nen seid.*

How we went ___ chang - ing coun - tries more of - ten than our shoes ___
Gin - gen wir doch öf - ters als die Schu - he *die Län - der wech - selnd*

do not hurry

through the wars of the class - es des - pair - ing to see in - just - ice and
durch die Klas - sen - krie - ge, *ver - zwei - felt wenn da nur Un - recht war und*

no in-dig-na-tion. ——
kei - ne Em-pö - rung. ——

do not hurry, quietly   25

And yet this we knew: ev-en hat-red of baseness dis-torts the
Da-bei wuss-ten wir doch: Auch der Hass ge-gen die Nie-drig-keit ver-zerrt die

accel.

fea-tures, ev-en rage a-gainst in-jus-tice makes the voice — hoarse. — We who
Zü - ge, auch der Zorn ge-gen das Un-recht macht die Stim-me hei - ser. Wir, die den

a tempo

wished to pre-pare — the — ground — for friend-li-ness, we
Bo-den be-rei-ten — woll-ten für Freund-lich-keit, wir

35

could — not our-selves — be — friend-ly.
konn - ten sel - ber nicht freund - lich sein.

But you —
Ihr a - ber,

when things have reached the point where — man is no long-er a
wenn es so weit ist, dass der Mensch dem Men-schen kein

40

wolf to man, — re-mem-ber us with for - bear-ance.
Wolf mehr ist, — ge-den-ket un - ser mit Nach-sicht.

Abortion Is Illegal

Ballade zum P. 218

Words by Bertolt Brecht; Music by Hanns Eisler;
English lyrics by Eric Bentley; ©1967 by Eric Bentley.

* If you have a tremendous reach, you can play Eisler's exact written piano notes on the guitar. 1st bar,
pinky on 7th fret of A string. 2nd bar, hold that while playing 3rd fret D string. 3rd bar, add open G
string, then bring pinky down to 5th fret A string. And so on. Or you may play the indicated chords in
brackets. Or skip the intro-interlude altogether and start with the singing.

The Mask of Wickedness

Die Maske des Bösen

Words by Bertolt Brecht; Music by Hanns Eisler;
English lyrics by Eric Bentley; ©1967 by Eric Bentley.

veins in his fore - head in - di - cat - ing what a strain ———— it
schwol - le - nen Stirn - a - dern, an - deu - tend: wie an - stren-gend

is to be wick - ed.
ist es, bö - se zu sein.

The Sprinkling of Gardens

Vom Sprengen des Gartens

Words by Bertolt Brecht; Music by Hanns Eisler; English lyrics by Eric Bentley; ©1964 by Eric Bentley.

O, sprink - ling of gar - dens, O, sprink - ling to en - cour - age green. Wa - ter - ing the thirs - ty bush - es give more than e - nough, give more, give — more, give more than e -

Oh, Spren - gen des Gar - tens, das Grün zu er - mu - ti - gen. Wäs - sern der durst-gen Bäu - me, gib mehr als ge - nug, gib mehr, gib — mehr, gib mehr als ge -

nough. And do not for-get the shrubb'-ry e-ven if it bears no

nug. *Und ver-giss auch nicht das Strauch-werk, auch das bee-ren-lo-se*

fruit and is worn out, Do not for-get be-tween the flow-ers

nicht, das er-mat-te-te, und ü-ber-sieh nicht zwi-schen den Blu-men

the weeds for they too feel thirst.

das Un-kraut, das auch Durst hat.

Now you may wa-ter just the fresh-est lawns,

Noch gies-se nur den fri-schen Ra-sen,

On the World's Kindness

Von der Freundlichkeit der Welt

The guitar may play this simply with a slow arpeggio* strum on the chords indicated. In that case, leave out the interlude which comes at the beginning and end and between the verses, or use the eighth-note repeated figure with a two-finger pluck on the second and third strings, as indicated in the diagram above the third bar. However, if you can read a little music and want to develop an interesting guitar part closer to the piano sounds as envisaged by Eisler, then forget about the indicated chords and build the whole part around the eighth-note motif. With your index and middle fingers plucking that, your thumb can handle the countermelody which enters in the bass at the seventh bar (or occasionally double the melody itself).

With the fourth verse, transfer the eighth-note motif to the second and fourth strings, with the middle or ring finger plucking the new countermelody high on the first string. The interlude, as written, is unplayable on guitar, but the descending bass line may be played while keeping the eighth-note dissonant moving along without pause. The B (no. 3) chord at the end may be useful elsewhere throughout the piece. As a variation in one verse, for instance, play that chord with three fingers and occasionally pluck the D or A string with the thumb.

Words by Bertolt Brecht; Music by Hanns Eisler; English lyrics by Eric Bentley; © 1956 by The New Republic.

* arpeggio: beginning with the thumb, pluck each string of the chord, one after the other.

No one called you, you were not besought.
In no handsome carriage were you brought.
On this earth you were quite unknown,
When a man placed your hand in his own.

And the world, it is not in your debt.
No one stops you, if you try to quit.
Many never gave you a thought, my dears!
Many too on your account shed tears.

Keiner schrie euch, ihr wart nicht begehrt,
Und man holte euch nicht im Gefährt.
Hier auf Erden wart ihr unbekannt,
Als ein Mann euch einst nahm an der Hand.

Und die Welt, die ist euch gar nichts schuld:
Keiner hält euch, wenn ihr gehen wollt.
Vielen, Kinder, wart ihr vielleicht gleich.
Viele aber weinten uber euch.

The Poplar Tree on Karlsplatz

Die Pappel vom Karlsplatz

Words by Bertolt Brecht; Music by Hanns Eisler;
English lyrics by Eric Bentley; ©1964 by Eric Bentley.

There's a pop - lar tree on Karls - platz
Ei - ne Pap - pel steht am Karls - platz

in the ru - ined ci - ty of Ber - lin, ____ And when peo - ple walk a - cross the
mit - ten in der Trüm - mer - stadt Ber - lin, ____ und wenn Leu - te ge - hen ü - bern

Karls - platz they all see its friend - ly green. ____
Karls - platz, se - hen sie ihr freund - lich Grün. ____

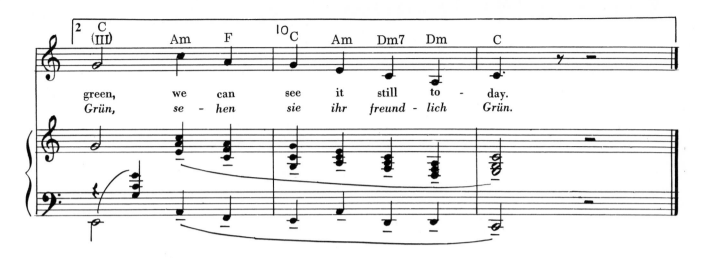

green,   we can   see   it   still   to - day.
Grün,   se - hen   sie   ihr   freund - lich   Grün.

Nineteen Forty-six in winter,
Men were freezing, wood was very rare.
Many trees were cut down on Karlsplatz,
And that was their final year.

But the poplar tree on Karlsplatz,
When spring comes around, is green and gay.
It's thanks to you, inhabitants of Karlsplatz,
That we see it still today.

In dem Winter sechs-und-vierzig
frorn die Menschen, und das Holz war rar,
und es fielen da viele Baume,
und es wurd' ihr letztes Jahr.

Doch die Pappel dort am Karlsplatz,
zeigt uns heute noch ihr grünes Blatt:
Seid bedankt, Anwohner vom Karlsplatz,
dass man sie noch immer hat.

How the Wind Blows

Wie der Wind weht

Words by Bertolt Brecht; Music by Hanns Eisler;
English lyrics by Eric Bentley; ©1967 by Eric Bentley.

Guitarists note the eighth-note doubling of the rhythm each time
the Db(Eb) chord comes along.

Happy the Man

Lenin-Zitat

Words by Bertolt Brecht; Music by Hanns Eisler;
English lyrics by Eric Bentley; ©1956. 1960, 1964 by
Eric Bentley.

Guitar capo up three frets.

Change the World: It Needs It

Ändere die Welt, sie braucht es

Words by Bertolt Brecht; Music by Hanns Eisler; English lyrics by Eric Bentley; ©1956,1960, 1964 by Eric Bentley.

Guitar play in Am. Capo up three frets.

Song of the Rice-Barge Coolies

Gesang der Reiskahnschlepper

Words by Bertolt Brecht; Music by Hanns Eisler;
English lyrics by Eric Bentley; © 1956, 1960, 1964 by
Eric Bentley.

Come Out and Fight

Streiklied

Words by Bertolt Brecht; Music by Hanns Eisler;
English lyrics by Eric Bentley; ©1956, 1960, 1964 by
Eric Bentley.

Strict strong March tempo

Come out, come out and fight them,
Komm her-aus, Ge-nos - se!

And risk the nick-le that's a nick-le no more. The
Ris - kier' den Pfen-nig, der kein Pfen-nig mehr ist, die

not e - nough guns; they've not e - nough guns! _____ Come
zi - sten nicht ge - nug Ge - weh - re! Her -

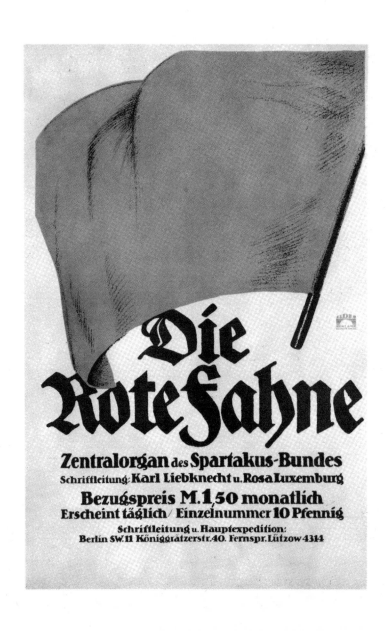

Supply and Demand

Lied des Händlers

Words by Bertolt Brecht; Music by Hanns Eisler; English lyrics by Eric Bentley; © 1956, 1960, 1964 by Eric Bentley.

For performance with piano it may be good to use the interlude (on pages 114 and 118) also as an introduction, as Eric Bentley does on his record, Songs of Hanns Eisler.

* This chord may be played by an index finger barre across strings 6, 5, 4, 3, and 2 from the 'wrong' (i.e. - top) side.

I on - ly know ___ its price!
ich ken - ne nur ih - ren Preis!

Men ___ take too much
So ein Mensch braucht zu viel

We Are the Scum of the Earth

Wir sind der Abschaum der Welt

Words by Bertolt Brecht; Music by Hanns Eisler;
English lyrics by Eric Bentley; ©1956, 1960, 1964 by
Eric Bentley.

Play guitar chords in parentheses, capo on first fret, during the
first two-thirds of the piece, through the words "Notice reads."
Then capo off fast and play chords as written.

Praise of Illegal Work

Lob der illegalen Arbeit

Words by Bertolt Brecht; Music by Hanns Eisler; English lyrics by Eric Bentley; ©1956, 1960, 1964 by Eric Bentley.

Guitar capo up two frets. Play chords in parentheses.

si - lence?
Schwei - gen?

But who would do it for si - lence?
A - ber wer tut's für das Schwei - gen?

* To enable the guitar to play the bass line of this ten bar section, the piano bass notes are indicated as the guitar would read them, with capo on second fret.

Praise of the U.S.S.R.

Lob der U.S.S.R.

Words by Bertolt Brecht; Music by Hanns Eisler; English lyrics by Eric Bentley; ©1956, 1960, 1964 by Eric Bentley.

Guitar capo up three frets and play chords in parentheses.

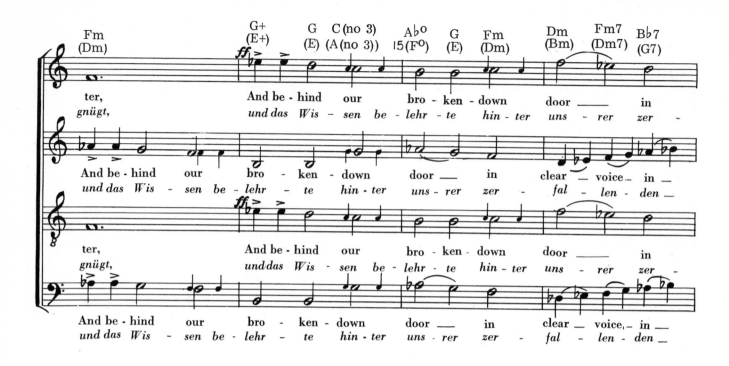

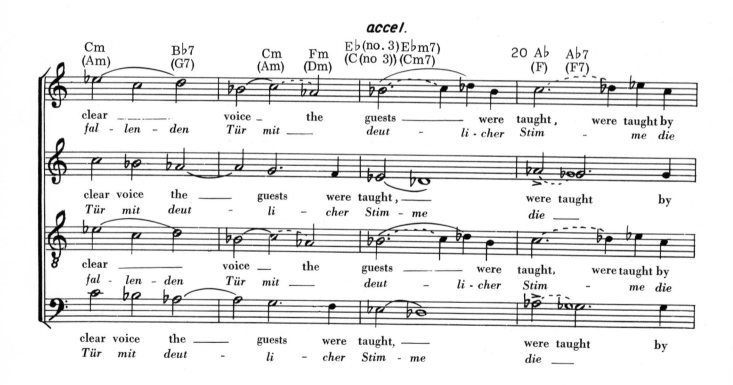

In Praise of Study

Lob der Lernens

Words by Bertolt Brecht; Music by Hanns Eisler;
English lyrics by Eric Bentley; ©1967 by Eric Bentley.

In this song, as with many of Eisler's, five or six string chords are not nearly as correct or effective as two, three, or four strings. Plucking with thumb and two or three fingers will most of the time be best. On the phrase, "You have to take over the leadership," full five or six string chords may be used in stronger contrast.

* Play F chord plus A (5th) string. Leave out 6th string.

On Suicide

Über den Selbstmord

Words by Bertolt Brecht; Music by Hanns Eisler;
English lyrics by Eric Bentley; ©1947, 1948, 1956,
1961, 1965 by Eric Bentley.

There's Nothing Quite Like Money

Lied der Kupplerin

Words by Bertolt Brecht; Music by Hanns Eisler;
English lyrics by Eric Bentley; ©1964 by Eric Bentley.

Suggest guitar um-pah style here in the beginning and at the end.
On the AbM7 chord, play the d 'um' and finger the chord for the
'pah.'

You'll love the sight of moonlight on the water
When you've got some money in your purse.
What's the use of man's or woman's beauty
If you're mean and simply won't disburse?
For a girl's knee only sags
At the sight of money bags.
Let me ask you a question, Mac:
Full of young love's ecstasy,
How should Jill and how should Jack
Make love on empty stomachs?
It cannot be done, alack.
Food's our central heat and money
Is our aphrodisiac.

Ach, was soll des roten Mondes Anblick
Auf dem Wasser, wenn der Zaster fehlt?
Und was soll da eines Mannes oder Weibes
  Schönheit
Wenn man knapp ist and es sich verhehlt.
Wo ich Liebe sah und schwache Knie
War's beim Anblick von -- Marie.
Und das ist bemerkenswert:
Wie soll er and wie soll sie
Sehnsuchtsvoll und unbeschwert
Auf den leeren Magen lieben?
Nein, mein Freund, das ist verkehrt.
Frass macht warm und Geld macht sinnlich
Wie uns die Erfahrung lehrt.

The Love Market

Lied eines Freudenmädchens

Words by Bertolt Brecht; Music by Hanns Eisler;
English lyrics by Eric Bentley; ©1964 by Eric Bentley.

Yes, you learn to play that market
With increased facility
Selling your embraces wholesale
Though your feelings may slowly fade away
If you hand 'em out too generously.
    God be praised, etc.

Study, as you may, that market
Haggle as you also may,
Selling kisses, and for peanuts,
Easy, that it ain't, still I've no complaint,
Though we don't get younger day by day.
    God be praised, etc.

Freilich geht es mit den Jahren,
Leichter auf den Liebesmarkt.
Und umarmt sie dort in Scharen,
Aber das Gefühl wird erstaunlich kühl
Wenn man damit allzuwenig kargt.
    Gottseidank, usw.

Und auch wenn man gut das Handeln,
Lernte auf der Liebesmess!:
Lust in Kleingeld zu verwandeln,
Fällt doch niemals leicht; ach, es wird erreicht,
Doch man wird auch älter unterdes.
    Gottseidank, usw

The Tree and the Branches

Ballade vom Baum und den Ästen

Words by Bertolt Brecht; Music by Hanns Eisler;
English lyrics by Eric Bentley; ©1964 by Eric Bentley.

still. / schweigt.
More! say the guests at tab-le, till the / Mehr her! sa-gen die Gä-ste, bis der

host shows them the bill. / And they bill. / Wirt die Rech-nung zeigt. / Und sie schweigt.

And they shoot off their big revolvers
At every capable head.
And they swagger up and down in pairs,
And they take their money from a cupboard
Which is now full of gold.
They are on the up and up.
This cupboard is forever full, said they.
And here we can live high off the hog, said
    they.
To the end of time.
Good! say all the branches,
But the tree trunk is still.
More! say the guests at the table,
Till the host shows them the bill.

Und sie schossen ihre Pistolen
In jeden besseren Kopf,
Und sie kamen mindestens zu zweit,
Und dann ging'n sie drei Mark abholen
Aus ihrem goldenen Topf.
Jetzt waren sie endlich so weit.
"Der wird immer schon voll bleiben,"
    sagten sie.
Bis ans Ende der Zeit,
Schon, so sagten die Äste.
Aber der Baumstamm schweigt.
Sturm kam peitschend die Gäste
Und den Wirt, der die Reichnung
    *verschweigt. ***

* The English follows an earlier version. The German here
means: "Storm came, whipping the guests and the host who
keeps quiet about the bill."

Ballad of Marie Sanders

Ballade von der Judenhure Marie Sanders

Words by Bertolt Brecht; Music by Hanns Eisler;
English lyrics by Eric Bentley; ©1964 by Eric Bentley.

* Julius Streicher, the anti-semite.

45

E+   **E**   **F6**   **Am**

com - ing!   make   room!   God a - bove, if men on - ly
re - det   heut'   Nacht.   Gros- ser Gott, wenn sie ein ___

Dm7   **E7**   50 **Am**

used their ears ___ they would know who does what and to whom. ___
Ohr hät - ten, ___ wüss - ten sie, was man mit ih - nen macht. ___

Do Not Cry, Marie!

Deutsches Lied, 1937

Words by Bertolt Brecht; Music by Hanns Eisler;
English lyrics by Eric Bentley; ©1967 by Eric Bentley.

Guitar plays chords in parenthesis. Capo up two frets.

The German Miserere

Das deutsche Miserere

Words by Bertolt Brecht; Music by Hanns Eisler;
English lyrics by Eric Bentley; ©1963 by Eric Bentley.

Once upon a time our leaders gave us orders
To go out and conquer the large town of Paris
So we invaded France and with our tanks and
    bombers
We conquered all of France in a few days.

Eines schöne Tages befahl'n uns're
    Obern
Das schönere Frankreich fur sie zu erobern.
Wir sind mit Tanks und Bombern
In Frankreich eigebrochen
Und haben es erobert in vier Wochen.

Song of a German Mother

Lied einer deutschen Mutter

Words by Bertolt Brecht; Music by Hanns Eisler; English lyrics by Eric Bentley; ©1944, 1963 by Eric Bentley.

My son, I gave you the jack-boots And the brown shirt came from me, But had I known what I now know ____ I'd have hanged ___ my-self, ___ I'd have hanged my-self from a tree. And

Mein Sohn, ich hab dir die Stie-fel und das brau - ne Hemd ge - schenkt, doch hätt' ich ge-wusst, was ich heut weiss, ____ hätt' ich mich' lie-ber, hätt' ich lie - ber mich auf - ge - hängt. Mein

did not com-plain or en-treat For I did not know what I
nicht da - ge - gen ge - stemmt. Denn ich wuss-te nicht, was ich

now know: — It was your wind - ing sheet.
heut weiss: — Es war dein To - ten - hemd.

And when I saw your arm, son,
Raised high in the Hitler salute,
I did not know all those arms, son,
Would wither, would wither, would wither at
    the root.

Mein Sohn, als ich deine Hand sah
Erhoben zum Hitlergruss,
Wusst ich nicht, dass dem, der ihn grüsset
Die Hand verdorren, die Hand verdorren
    muss.

A German at Stalingrad

Und ich werde nicht mehr sehen

Words by Bertolt Brecht; Music by Hanns Eisler;
English lyrics by Eric Bentley; ©1944 by Rocky Mountain Press.

More quietly, held back

noise of the town   nor ———— its   un - hap - py noise.
Lärm der Stadt   *o - der den*   *bit - ter - en.* ————

slight rit.

Song of the Little Wind

Lied vom kleinen Wind

Words by Bertolt Brecht; Music by Hanns Eisler;
English lyrics by Eric Bentley; ©1967 by Eric Bentley.

Guitar capo up one fret. For the first eight bars, the guitar may
wish to play the two-note trills indicated (same notes as the
piano plays. If not, then play the chords in parentheses. From
the ninth bar on, a slow um-pah is indicated.)

Oh, reaper, stop now and have done!
Let one stalk remain upright!
Don't drink your wine all at one gulp,
And don't kiss me in flight.

Such a little wind, it's hardly there,
Just a rocking in the air,
Like what the plums want from the tree:
On the ground they want to be.

Ach, Schnitter, lass es sein genug,
Lass, Schnitter, ein'n Halm stehen.
Trink nicht dein Wein auf einen Zug
Und küss mich nicht im Gehen.

So ein kleiner Wind du spürst ihn kaum,
'S ist wie ein sanftes Wiegen.
Die Pflaumen wolln ja so vom Baum
Woll'n auf dem Boden liegen.

And What Did She Get?

Das Lied vom Weib des Nazisoldaten

Words by Bertolt Brecht; Music by Hanns Eisler;
English lyrics by Eric Bentley; ©1964 by Eric Bentley.

Allegretto

And what did she get, that sol-dier's wife, from the an-cient cit-y of
Prague? _____ From Prague she got the but-ton shoes, Lots
of good news and but-ton shoes. _____ And that

Und was be-kam des Sol-da-ten Weib aus der al-ten Haupt-stadt
Prag? _____ Aus Prag be-kam sie die Stö-ckel-schuh, ei-nen
Gruss und da-zu die Stö-ckel-schuh _____ das be-

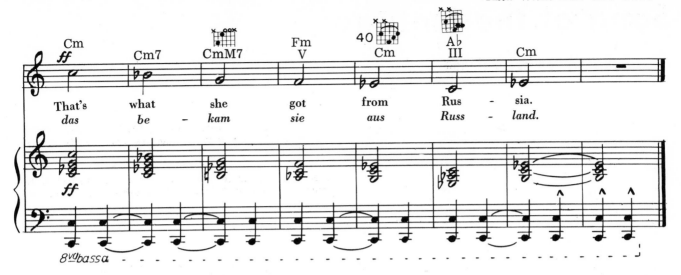

Cm   Cm7   CmM7   Fm   40   Cm   A♭   Cm

V   III

That's   what   she   got   from   Rus   -   sia.
das   be   -   kam   sie   aus   Russ   -   land.

And what did she get, that soldier's wife
From the rich town Amsterdam?
From Amsterdam she got the hat
It knocked them flat, the new Dutch hat:
That is what she got from Amsterdam.

And what did she get, that soldier's wife
From Paris, city of light?
She got the gown with the silken sheen
The girls turned green at the silken sheen
And that is what she got from Paris.

Und was bekam des Soldaten Weib
Aus dem reichen Amsterdam?
Aus Amsterdam bekam sie den Hut
Und er steht ihr gut, der holländische Hut
Den bekam sie aus Amsterdam.

Und was bekam des Soldaten Weib
Aus der Lichterstadt Paris?
Aus Paris bekam sie das seidene Kleid,
Zu der Nachbarin Neid das seidene Kleid
Das bekam sie aus Paris.

Song of the Moldau

Das Lied von der Moldau

Words by Bertolt Brecht; Music by Hanns Eisler;
English lyrics by Eric Bentley; ©1964 by Eric Bentley.

Guitar capo up three frets. Play chords in parentheses. The
arpeggio style may be used all through this song if desired.

On the bed ___ of the Mol - dau the
Am Grun - de der Mol - dau

peb - bles are stir - ring. In Prague ___ three em - per
wan - dern die Stei - ne, es lie - gen drei Kai - ser be -

ors ___ lie dead. ___ The big ___ will not stay big, the
gra - ben in Prag. ___ Das Gros - se bleibt gross nicht und

* The arpeggio feeling in these two bars may be approcahed on guitar by beginning each of the chords in
( ) on the low E (6th) string.

NOTES ON THE SONGS

by Eric Bentley

Coal for Mike. The theme is taken from Chapter 12, Book 4 of Sherwood Anderson's "Poor White."

The Gray Goose. This Southern folk song was in the repertoire of Leadbelly. Brecht seems to have infused into it a social content not always, if ever, present in American versions. In the American, it is not a "Herr" (gentleman, boss) who goes hunting but "my daddy" or, in some versions, "the parson." The German does not even have the "Lord, Lord" which suggests a religious background but, instead, a "ja ja ja" meant to suggest the goose's cry.

Solidarity Song. Dates back to 1930, and was sung in the film "Kuhle Wampe" ("Whither Germany?"). Proved also a source of confusion in the discussion between Brecht and the Un-American Activities Committee in 1947.

Song of the United Front. Hanns Eisler states: "It was written in London in 1936. Because, with the Popular Front Congress, the question of the unity of the workers again was important, Brecht phoned me and said a song must be written about this. The next day already Ernst Busch was singing it in English."

All or Nothing. Written in the Thirties, this song was later incorporated in Brecht's play, "Days of the Commune." The alternative: guns or chains! proposed in the German has been dropped from this English version, since this is a book of songs for use today and not a historical document. "Guns or chains" was a different thing in the days of the commune from what it is in the days of Martin Luther King.

Song of the Soldier. Published in "Manual of Piety" in 1927, this poem found its way later into "Mother Courage." The locale in the text Eisler used was Russia (there is a reference to the Volga); later this was changed to Germany; it makes no difference.

Peace Song. Brecht took this song from a poem by Pablo Neruda. The sixth strophe was added by Eric Bentley in 1966. Unlike other songs in this book, it is not given in two languages throughout, but alternately in German and English.

Easter Sunday. In the middle Thirties, when this poem was written, Brecht was living on a Danish island.

The Little Radio. The boats and trains took Brecht from Germany to his Danish island, and thence to Sweden and Finland. It was in Finland that he got his visa to the U.S. in 1941.

And the Times are Dark. Again the subject is Brecht's period in Scandinavia (1933-1941).

Homecoming. Home was Augsburg. The poem was written in America at a time when the U.S. airforce was strafing the German cities.

A Hollywood Elegy. While living in Santa Monica, Brecht wrote a group of Hollywood Elegies. Sometimes he was helped by friends to put them into English, and this one has survived in English alone. (It is the only English lyric in this book not by me.)

To Those Who Come After: Three Elegies. This tripartite poem is one of Brecht's finest and most celebrated works; I have done another translation, for reading, which does not fit the Eisler music: it is published in "The German Theatre Today," ed. Shaw, University of Texas Press, 1963.

Abortion Is Illegal. The German title, literally translated, is "Ballad of Paragraph 218," the paragraph in the Weimar Constitution (1918-1933) that imposed heavy penalties for abortion. This song was found particularly shocking by the Unamerican Activities Committee in 1947, and for that matter has not been published in the German Democratic Republic of today.

The Mask of Wickedness. A poem in the manner of Arthur Waley's translations from the Chinese.

The Sprinkling of Gardens. "Lyric" in the conventional sense, this poem remains Brechtian in the emphasis given to the weeds and the naked ground.

On the World's Kindness. An early poem of Brecht's characterized by a delicacy of feeling and mood of reconciliation which some would consider "not Brechtian."

The Poplar Tree on Karlsplatz. Visiting East Berlin in 1965, I found Karlplatz or Karlsplatz, but did not find any old poplar tree -- only several newly-planted ones. Either the tree mentioned by Brecht has also been cut down, or the poet invented this story.

How the Wind Blows. This poem is dedicated to Ernst Bloch, the left-wing philosopher who "defected" from East Germany after Brecht's death. Brecht, like Bloch, was critical of the bureaucrats of the East German regime. He was also inclined to criticize the German people as a whole for their inability to have fun.

Happy The Man, Change the World: It Needs It, Song of the Rice-Barge Coolies, Come Out and Fight, Supply and Demand, We Are the Scum of the Earth, Praise of the USSR, and Praise of Illegal Work are all from the play, "The Measures Taken." The complete text of the play is in print in "The Modern Theater," Vol. 6, Doubleday Anchor Books, and elsewhere.

In Praise of Study is from the play, "The Mother," which was performed in New York in 1935 as adapted by Paul Peters. As translated by Lee Baxandall, it was published by Grove Press in 1965.

The Love Market and There's Nothing Quite Like Money are in "Round Heads." A translation of "Round Heads and

WITHDRAWN
COLLEGE LIBRARY
DENTON, TEXAS